בס"ד
לד' הארץ ומלואה

This book belongs to:

Please read it to me!

Time to Start a Brand New Year

This book was written for the students of the
Charlotte Jewish Day School. Love, Morah Rochel

Dedicated to my dear wife Fern, and to Avraham Moshe,
Rochel Chana & Moshe, Naftoli Simcha and Chaya Baila,
for making my life's happiness "Brand New" every day! S.S.

First Edition – Elul 5775 / August 2015
Copyright © 2015 by
HACHAI PUBLISHING
ALL RIGHTS RESERVED

Editor: D.L. Rosenfeld
Managing Editor: Yossi Leverton
Layout: Moshe Cohen

ISBN 978-1-929628-53-7
LCCN: 2015906584

HACHAI PUBLISHING
Brooklyn, New York
Tel: 718-633-0100 - Fax: 718-633-0103
www.hachai.com - info@hachai.com

Printed in China

GLOSSARY

Challah......................	Loaves of bread for the Sabbath and Jewish holidays
L'Shanah Tovah........	Phrase used to wish others a good new year
Mitzvos......................	Commandments; good deeds
Rosh Hashanah........	Jewish New Year
Shofar.......................	Ram's horn
Tashlich....................	Prayer recited near a body of water on Rosh Hashanah

Time to Start a Brand New Year

by Rochel Groner Vorst
illustrated by Shepsil Scheinberg

Hachai PUBLISHING

We are Rosh Hashanah blowing,
See us picking, tasting, throwing?
Busy dipping, baking, sending,
As this year is almost ending!

Apple tree, apple tree,
Have you anything for me?
Rosh Hashanah's almost here,
Time to start a brand new year!

I have apples everywhere,
Ripe and ready, here and there.
Choose the biggest one you see,
A present from the apple tree!

Honeybee, honeybee,
Have you anything for me?
Rosh Hashanah's almost here,
Time to start a brand new year!

I have honey, gold and sweet
For a sticky New Year's treat.
Pour my honey in a dish,
Dip your apple; make a wish!

We are Rosh Hashanah sending,
See us writing, cutting, bending?

Now we're stamping, sticking, folding
All the envelopes we're holding!

Mailman, mailman,
Driving in your mail van,
We have lots of cards right here
To wish our friends a good new year!

Challah bakers, challah bakers,
Where are all those challah makers?
Rosh Hashanah's almost here,
Time to start a brand new year!

We are Rosh Hashanah baking,
See us sifting, mixing, taking?
Lots of shaping, brushing, rising –

Raisins in it? How surprising!

Now we're spreading, putting, getting,
We are Rosh Hashanah setting
For the guests we are inviting.
Candles ready – time for lighting!

Rosh Hashanah, now you're here.
"Have a happy, sweet New Year!"

Pomegranate, red and round,
What is underneath your crown?
One seed, two seeds, three seeds, four,
And I have so many more!

Tipping, tapping down the street,
New shoes shining on our feet.
We are Rosh Hashanah going,
Time to hear the shofar blowing!

Shofar with your rousing sound,
I can hear you all around,
Calling, "Rosh Hashanah's here,
Time to start a brand new year!"

תקיעה
שברים~תרועה
תקיעה

We are Rosh Hashanah walking,
See us marching, strolling, talking?

We'll be reaching, throwing, shaking,

On this Tashlich trip we're taking!

Say goodbye to each mistake,
Throw it in the flowing lake.

So glad Rosh Hashanah's here,
Time to start a brand new year!

We are Rosh Hashanah packing,
Busy piling up and stacking
All the mitzvos that we've done
For the year that's just begun.

L'Shanah Tovah!

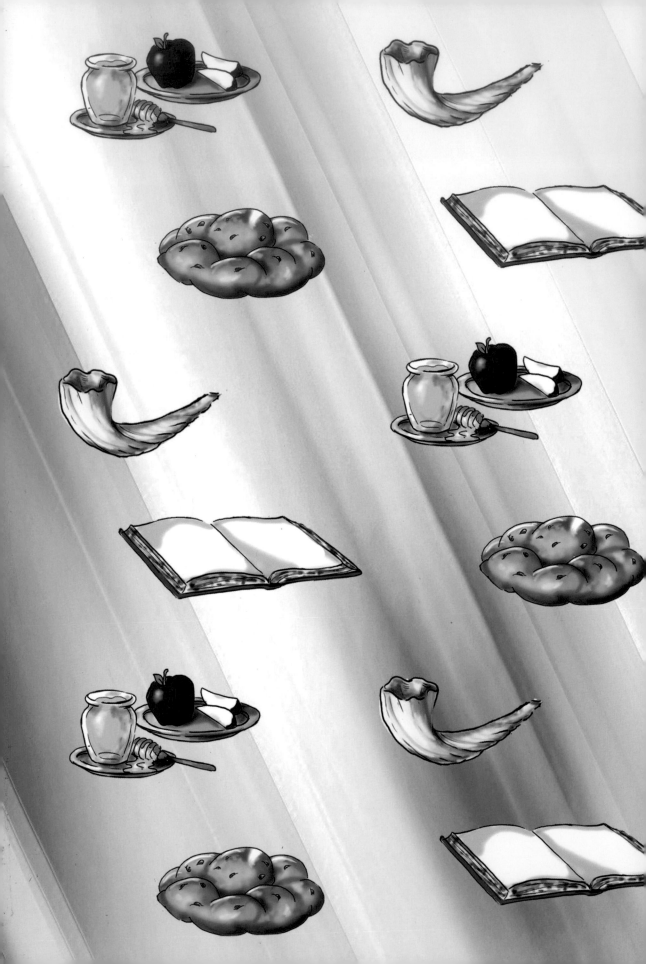